Under the mango tree
songs and poems
for primary schools

edited by Mabel Segun and Neville Grant

Book 2

Illustrated by Maureen and Gordon Gray

Longman

Longman Group UK Limited,
Longman House, Burnt Mill, Harlow,
Essex CM20 2JE, England
and Associated Companies throughout the world.

First published 1980
Eighth impression 1994

Set in Spectrum (Monophoto)

Printed in China
PPC/08

ISBN 0 582 59520 7

Contents

Introduction

As in *Under the mango tree* Book 1, Book 2 includes not only some old favourites, but also a large number of traditional songs and poems, most of which hitherto have not been very accessible. In addition, this book contains some quite new material. All the poems and songs have been written or selected mainly for their enjoyment value, but, of course, since poetry is poetry, they often have other functions as well.

The poems in Book 2 come from many different parts of Africa and the world, including Nigeria, Ghana, Sierra Leone, Kenya, Tanzania, Uganda, Southern Africa, the USA, Cuba, and England. Many of the poems were not originally composed in the English language. Items translated from the following languages will be found in these pages: Kiswahili, Hausa, Yoruba, Igbo, Akan, Fulfulde, Krio, Kikuyu, Kikamba, Dholuo, Ganda, Spanish and French; and some other languages.

Some of the poems were written by children. It is hoped that this little anthology will help to stimulate an interest not only in poetry in general, and African poetry in particular, but also in the writing and translation of poems – by teacher and pupil alike! But a word of warning: translation is well worth attempting, but if a translator aims at trying to capture, almost word for word, the literal meaning of the original, he will end up with something of only academic interest: one should try to capture the *spirit* of the original, and where possible, the *rhythm* and *sound*. This means that translations have to be *creative*, not merely literal. The aim should be to enable those who do not speak the original language to enjoy the poem almost as much as the native speakers of the original language. In this way, the English language can help all of us to enjoy the literature, oral or written, of other cultures, both within the African continent, and beyond.

Suggestions on classroom treatment of these poems may be found in the Teacher's notes at the back of the book.

1   Under the mango tree

Old Juma is dead and laid in his grave,
  Laid in his grave, laid in his grave;
Old Juma is dead and laid in his grave,
  H'm ha! laid in his grave.

They planted a mango tree over his head,
  Over his head, over his head;
They planted a mango tree over his head,
  H'm ha! over his head.

The mangoes grew ripe and ready to fall,
  Ready to fall, ready to fall;
The mangoes grew ripe and ready to fall,
  H'm ha! ready to fall.

There came an old woman a-picking them all,
  A-picking them all, a-picking them all;
There came an old woman a-picking them all,
  H'm ha! picking them all.

Old Juma jumps up and gives her a knock,
  Gives her a knock, gives her a knock;
Which makes the old woman go hipperty-hop,
  H'm ha! hipperty hop.

2　Fine, big yam

Fine big yam,
Fine big yam,
Heavy in the hand,
Heavy in the hand,
If it had been firewood
You would have complained,
Far too heavy, your neck
would have strained,
But this isn't firewood,
It gives you no pain!
It's fine, big yam,
Fine, big yam!

Fine big yam,
Fine big yam,
Finest in the land,
Finest in the land,
Your back bent to grow it
And now it's grown,
You worked hard to hoe it
And now it's home,
You feel proud to show it
And now it's shown!
It's fine big yam,
Fine big yam.

Neville Grant

3   Lullaby

Someone would like to have you for her child
but you are mine.
Someone would like to rear you on a costly mat
but you are mine.
Someone would like to place you on a camel blanket
but you are mine.
I have you to rear on a torn old mat.
Someone would like to have you as her child
but you are mine.

Akan

4   Kikuyu lullaby

Who has beaten you, Irungu,
    Urururu Irungu-i!
May thorn-bushes surround his room,
    Urururu Irungu-i!
Here's oil, don't cry, Irungu,
    Urururu Irungu-i!
Bananas and some gruel,
    Urururu Irungu-i!

3

5 Song of a motherless child

My father's wife, my father's wife	Nda
Bought apples in the market	Nda
Saliva wetted my chest	Nda
My eyes got stuck to the apples	Nda
But one does not eat meat with one's eyes	Nda
My father's wife ate up all the apples;	Nda
I then called on my God and Destiny	Nda
To plant an apple for me.	Nda
My apple! Grow, grow fast,	Nda
That a motherless one may eat an apple	Nda
That a bald-headed child may eat an apple.	Nda

Igbo

4

6 Riddles

The pictures on this page will help you to find the answers to these riddles!

1 Who is she? Wherever she goes,
   She's always changing her clothes.

2 What is always cooked before it is scraped,
   And always scraped before it is eaten?

3 What is it? A large black bird with
   sweet intestines.

4 What has teeth which can't bite,
   That we use every day;
   But once its teeth are broken,
   Then we throw it away?

5 Who is the man who never
   sleeps hungry?

6 I know of a beautiful hill –
   That no one can cultivate,
   Whatever his skill!

7 I have a wife – and all her children
   have beards!

8 What is it that dies if it takes water,
   and gets its life from the wind?

Make up some riddles for yourself, or translate them from your language. Who can make up a riddle that no one can answer?

7　The lazy farmer

There was a man named Ibejimato,
Whose head was like a bad tomato,
He did no work, his cutlass was rusty,
His house was dirty, his compound dusty.
One day he started to beat his wife
For leading such a lazy life.
She answered back, and soon their fight
Made all the chickens run in fright!

His wife ran off, the neighbours came,
And said the husband was to blame:
"Ibeji-beji-bejimato,
Your head is like a bad tomato!
A lazy man makes a lazy wife,
It's *you* who leads a lazy life!
Take your cutlass and dig your yams,
And then she'll help with willing hands."

Neville Grant (based on an *oro* song)

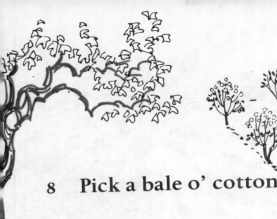

8   Pick a bale o' cotton

Jump down, turn around,
Pick a bale o' cotton,
Jump down, turn around,
Pick a bale a day.

Me an' my pardner can
Pick a bale o' cotton,
Me an' my pardner can
Pick a bale a day.

I had a little woman could
Pick a bale o' cotton,
I had a little woman could
Pick a bale a day.

Pick-a, pick-a, pick-a, pick-a,
Pick a bale o' cotton,
Pick-a, pick-a, pick-a, pick-a,
Pick a bale a day.

9 Mountain, let me pass

Mountain, mountain, come down and let me pass.
If you don't come down, I can't pass to where I'm going.
So I beg you come down and let me pass.
If you let me pass, I will give you twenty pesewas.
Mountain, I beg you please come down.
Come down, come down.
If you don't come down, I will throw stones at you.
So please come down for me to pass and go to where I am going.

Samuel Adatsi (Aged 12)

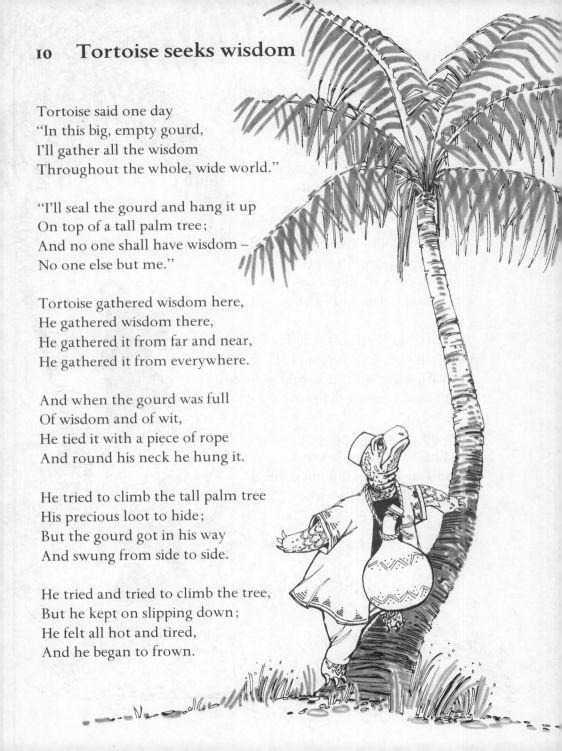

10   Tortoise seeks wisdom

Tortoise said one day
"In this big, empty gourd,
I'll gather all the wisdom
Throughout the whole, wide world."

"I'll seal the gourd and hang it up
On top of a tall palm tree;
And no one shall have wisdom –
No one else but me."

Tortoise gathered wisdom here,
He gathered wisdom there,
He gathered it from far and near,
He gathered it from everywhere.

And when the gourd was full
Of wisdom and of wit,
He tied it with a piece of rope
And round his neck he hung it.

He tried to climb the tall palm tree
His precious loot to hide;
But the gourd got in his way
And swung from side to side.

He tried and tried to climb the tree,
But he kept on slipping down;
He felt all hot and tired,
And he began to frown.

A stranger came along and asked,
"What is that you're trying?
And what have you got in that gourd?
Why, you're almost crying!"

Said Tortoise, "In this gourd I've put
All the wisdom under the sun,
And on this treē I'll hàng it
And be the only wise one."

"Your poor fool!" the stranger said,
"Surely you know it's true,
That you cannot climb a tree
With a load in front of you?"

"Let that gourd rest on your back
And then you can freely move!"
And with these words the stranger went –
What a fool Tortoise did prove!

From his neck he took the gourd
And broke it without a word,
For now he knew it did not contain
All the wisdom in the world.

Mabel Segun

11   Tintingun

(Refrain from a Yoruba folk tale about the Tortoise)

There was this vegetable
Tintingun!
That I gave to my wife
Tintingun!
To make into a stew
Tintingun!
But not to taste of it;
Tintingun!
My wife Yanrinbo
Tintingun!
Went and tasted it;
Tintingun!
And after, ate it all!
Tintingun!

As I pulled out my sword
She got hold of a stick
Tintingun!
The stick they call Orogun
Tintingun!
Hit me right on the head – gboin!
Tintingun!
And so it's goodbye forever!
Tintingun!
I'm never coming back!
Tintingun!

Mabel Segun (translated)

12   Crossing a busy street

The streets of Lagos are so busy,
It's not at all easy
To cross them without care –
There's traffic everywhere.

The cars that roar past
Are often very fast;
You have to be very smart,
But you must never dart.

Obey the Highway Code
Whenever you cross a road;
And remember what your parents say –
Never go into the streets to play.

Omowunmi Segun (Aged 12)

13   When it is raining

When it is raining,
The streets are wet;
Some people carry umbrellas,
Others wear raincoats;
Some run home as fast as they can,
And children stay indoors
Because their mothers say they should,
Or they might

       catch

         a

          cold.

Femi Segun (Aged 8)

14   When the electric lights are out

Electric lights are out?
Then bring us some candles;
No candles in the house?
Then open the windows;
The smiling moon
The twinkling stars
Will give us light enough.

Oluwole Adejare (adapted)

13

15   The trouble-lover

Ojo is his name,
Ojo the Trouble-Lover.
He loudly calls to Trouble
When Trouble is passing by;
He invites a rascal to his house
Just for love of quarrelling.

He pauses not before he fights
A person who argues with him;
Whenever he hears a quarrel going on,
Or sees some people exchanging blows,
He jumps into their midst –
All for love of quarrelling.

The Trouble-Lover says to you,
"I want to sit with you,"
If you reply, "There is no room"
He will retort, "Sure there's room
For me to sit – on top of your head." –
Just to start some quarrelling.

Trouble-Lover has no rest
No rest by day or night;
He looks for trouble here,
He looks for trouble there,
He looks for trouble everywhere –
All for love of quarrelling.

Adeboye Babalola (adapted)

16   Rain music

On the dusty earth-drum
Beats the falling rain;
Now a whispered murmur,
Now a louder strain.

Slender, silvery drumsticks,
On an ancient drum,
Beat the mellow music
Bidding life to come.

Chords of earth awakened,
Notes of greening spring,
Rise and fall triumphant
Over everything.

Slender, silvery drumsticks
Beat the long tattoo –
God, the Great Musician,
Calling life anew.

Joseph S. Cotter (Jnr.)

17   The flower is broken

The flower is broken
and the tree is standing.
The banana is talking
and the cassava is singing.
The green is crying.

Joel Mensah (Aged 12)

18   A male lion, I roar

I roar again, O hunters, listen
I am looking for the gentlemen
With weapons on the shoulder,
How is it that I haven't seen them yet?
What has prevented them?
You who are in hiding, come out,
Let us know the ripe from the raw.

I speak to you, O men
Who came to the hunt
And made me wild
So that I came out of the bush,
Why are you so far away now?
You do not come forward, why do you fear
You who are in hiding, come out,
Let us know the ripe from the raw.

Make good bullets,
Leave aside those bad ones,
And arrows for piercing me;
Fill them up in the quiver,
When you come let me eat up your flesh,
After finishing the entrails,
You who are in hiding, come out,
Let us know the ripe from the raw.

Ahmed Nassir Bin Juma Bhalo

19   You will walk in peace

You will walk in peace
Through the night,
When you go,
N'dila ho, do not listen
To the voices of the owls
Because
They tell of death.

You will walk in peace.
Through the night
On your way, N'dila ho
If you meet a mole
If you smell a certain root
Used when bodies are embalmed
What they foretell is death.

You will sleep in peace
Through the night.
If you hear your name
If you hear a low knock on your door
Never never never answer
For
Death is watching you.

You will always be in peace,
O N'dila ho, if you sneeze
During the day;
At night,
Sneezing is an evil sign.

Martial Sinda

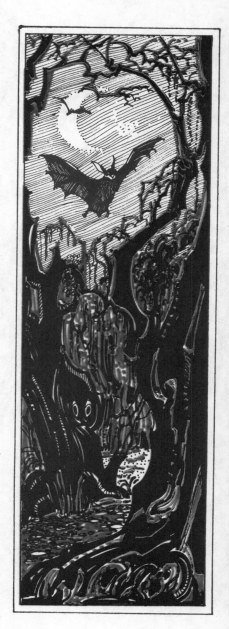

The hairy toe

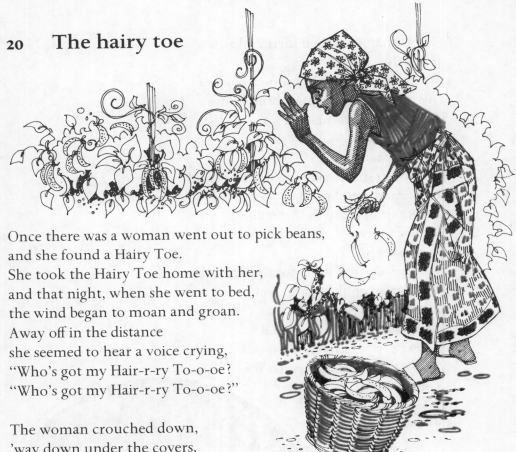

Once there was a woman went out to pick beans,
and she found a Hairy Toe.
She took the Hairy Toe home with her,
and that night, when she went to bed,
the wind began to moan and groan.
Away off in the distance
she seemed to hear a voice crying,
"Who's got my Hair-r-ry To-o-oe?
"Who's got my Hair-r-ry To-o-oe?"

The woman crouched down,
'way down under the covers,
and about that time
the wind appeared to hit the house,
smoosh,
and the old house creaked and cracked
like something was trying to get in.
The voice had come nearer,
almost at the door now,
and it said,
"Where's my Hair-r-ry To-o-oe?
"Who's got my Hair-r-ry To-o-oe?"

The woman crouched further down
under the covers
and pulled them tight around her head.
The wind growled around the house
Like some big animal
and r-r-umbled
over the chimney.
All at once she heard the door cr-r-a-ack
and Something slipped in
and began to creep over the floor.
The floor went
cre-e-eak, cre-e-eak
at every step that thing took towards her bed.
The woman could almost feel
it bending over her bed.
Then in an awful voice it said:
"Where's my Hair-r-ry To-o-oe?
"Who's got my Hair-r-ry To-o-oe?
"You've got it!"

Traditional American

21 The snake-man and the girl

[*Story-teller*] A beautiful girl lived long ago
Whose favourite word was always "NO".
One day while she was pounding yam
There came to her a strong young man:

[*First man*] Will you, won't you, will you, won't you,
Will you marry me?

[*Girl*] No, no, no, I'll never marry you
For you're too tall for me.

[*Story-teller*] One day while she was sweeping the floor,
There came to her a man once more:

[*Second man*] Will you, won't you, will you, won't you,
Will you marry me?

[*Girl*] No, no, no, I'll never marry you
For you're too fat for me.

[*Story-teller*]	The whole family complained:
[*Family*]	She will not marry this man, She will not marry that, She always says they are too tall, Or thin or short or fat!
[*Story-teller*]	Near the village there was a lake, And near the lake there was a cave, And in the cave there lived a snake, Who hissed:
[*Snake-man*]	I want a slave!
[*Story-teller*]	He hissed and strained And puffed and pained At last some legs he grew, He hung his tail inside the cave, And went the girl to woo.

[*Snake-man*]	Will you, won't you, will you, won't you, Will you marry me?
[*Girl*]	You're not too fat, You're not too thin, You're not too tall or small, Yes, you're fine, so please come in, And meet my family.
[*Snake-man*]	Oh, sir, you do not know my family, For we are nomads new from Tamale. But here's the bride-price, cowries and gold, Collected from the cattle I've sold.
[*Father*]	Young man, you are welcome to our land, And also to my daughter's hand.
[*Story-teller*]	Everyone was delighted.

[All (singing, dancing and clapping.)]

She would not marry this man,
She would not marry that,
She always said they were too tall,
Or thin, or short, or fat!
But now she's married, let's have a feast,
And pray they have ten children at least!

[Story-teller]

He took her back with him to the lake
And brought her to his cave,
He turned himself back into a snake,
And hissed:

[Snake-man]

Now you're my slave!

[Story-teller]

Oh, how she cried!
She nearly died!
But there was no escape.

24

She worked and wept,
She wept and worked,
With that horrible, ugly snake!
One day, the snake went out to hunt,
Leaving the girl alone.
She went out to the waterfront,
And she began to moan:

[*Girl*]   I will not stay longer with this snake,
In this horrible, dark cave.
I'd rather drown myself in the lake,
Than stay and be his slave.

[*Bird*]   Pretty girl, don't worry,
To the village I'll hurry,
I'll help you to escape
From that horrible snake!

[*Girl*]   Oh, thank you!
Thank you, pretty bird!

[*Story-teller*]	To the village flew the bird And told them all that she had heard.
[*Bird*]	Hurry! Hurry! Save your daughter! She's with the snake-man near the water. Hurry! Help her to escape, Before she's eaten by the snake!
[*Men*]	To arms! To arms!
[*Story-teller*]	The men replied.
[*Men*]	To arms, without delay!
[*Women*]	Oh, hurry, hurry!
[*Story-teller*]	The women cried,

[Women]	Save her, now, today!

[Story-teller]
(All clap in time
with the words as
the men and snake
do the dance of
the chase.)

Over the fields with swords and shields
They ran to the lake to kill the snake!
The snake went this way, the snake went that;
The men went this way, the men went that;
From the cave to the lake,
From the lake to the cave,
Till they killed the snake,
And the girl was saved!

[All (singing,
dancing and
clapping.)]

She would not marry this man,
She would not marry that!
She always said they were too tall,
Or thin, or short, or fat!
But now she's been saved by our fine young men,
Let's hope she'll see sense, and marry again!

Neville Grant

22　Mocking song

Tell me, woman, I ask you,
Can your husband dance?
Tell me, woman, answer me,
How does your husband dance?

Oh my God, all he can do
Is to sit and eat.
Ever since I married him
He hasn't moved his feet.

Ah, the glutton!

Sudan

23　The lazy man

When the cock crows,
the lazy man smacks his lips and says:
So it is daylight again, is it?
And before he turns over heavily,
before he even stretches himself,
before he even yawns –
the farmer has reached the farm,
the water-carriers arrived at the river,
the spinners are spinning their cotton,
the weaver works on his cloth,
and the fire blazes in the blacksmith's hut.

28

The lazy one knows where the soup is sweet
he goes from house to house.
If there is no sacrifice today,
his breast bone will stick out!
But when he sees the free yam,
he starts to unbutton his shirt,
he moves close to the celebrant.
Yet his troubles are not few.
When his wives reach puberty,
rich men will help him to marry them.

Yoruba

29

24 My lively young man

There was a young man from our village,
Who was full of joy and gladness,
This young man from our village.

A lively, friendly young man was he,
Full of life and fun,
This lively young man from our village.

This lively, fun-loving young man
Filled the whole village with laughter,
This fun-loving young man from our village.

In search of adventure he left,
He left our peaceful village,
This adventurous young man left our village.

He went to seek his fortune,
And found himself a job,
In the city, far far from our village!

He became a city man
Enjoying noisy parties,
This lively young man in the city.

Wild life, and drinks he loved,
And lively young friends too,
This lively young man in the city.

One night he went for a drive,
This popular, lively young man,
For a lively drive in the city.

He'd had a drink or two,
Or three, or four, or more,
That thirsty young man in the city.

A mad, drunken drive it was; and now,
That young man, that lively, fun-loving young man,
Is a DEAD young man in the city.

Modupe Oyedele (adapted)

25 Hausa song

Patience, patience, friend,
Marriage doesn't kill one.

Up the kapok and palm tree she climbed
To escape marriage, but could not.

Patience, patience, friend,
Marriage doesn't kill one.

For if it did so,
It would have killed a hundred maidens.

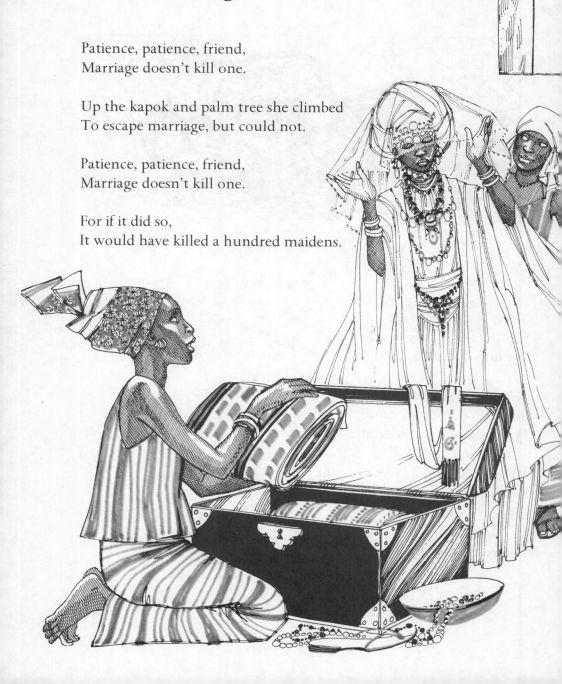

Patience, patience, friend,
Marriage doesn't kill one.

Up the ladder and upstairs she went
To escape marriage, but could not.

Patience, patience, friend,
Marriage doesn't kill one.

Into the train and into the car she went
To escape marriage, but could not.

Hausa

26   Song by a woman giving birth

My heart is joyful,
My heart flies away, singing,
Under the trees of the forest,
Forest our home and our mother,

In my net I have caught
A little bird.
My heart is caught in the net,
In the net with the bird.

Pygmy

27 Praise of a child

A child is like a rare bird.
A child is precious like coral.
A child is precious like brass
You cannot buy a child on the market.
Not for all the money in the world.
The child you can buy for money is a slave.
We may have twenty slaves,
We may have thirty labourers,
Only a child brings us joy,
One's child is one's child.
The buttocks of our child are not so flat
That we should tie the beads on another child's hips.
One's child is one's child
It may have a watery head or a square head,
One's child is one's child.
It is better to leave behind a child,
Than let the slaves inherit one's house.
One must not rejoice too soon over a child.
Only the one who is buried by his child,
Is the one who has truly borne a child.
On the day of our death, our hand cannot hold a single cowry.
We need a child to inherit our belongings.

Yoruba

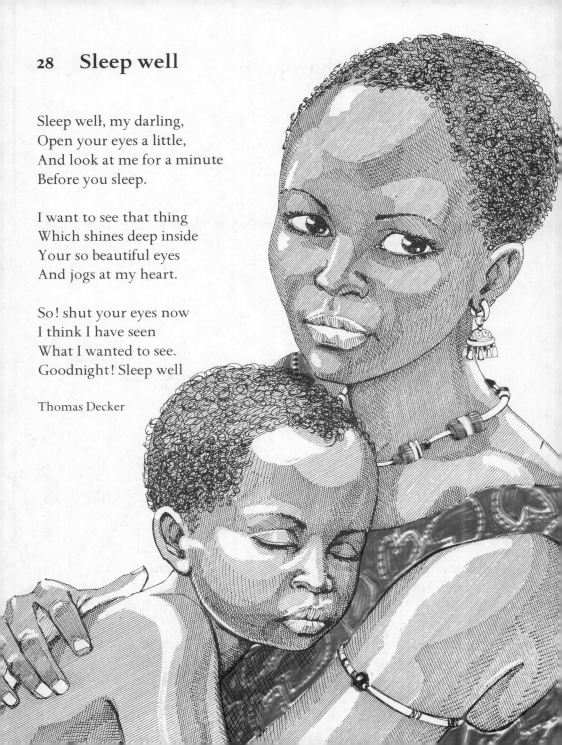

28 Sleep well

Sleep well, my darling,
Open your eyes a little,
And look at me for a minute
Before you sleep.

I want to see that thing
Which shines deep inside
Your so beautiful eyes
And jogs at my heart.

So! shut your eyes now
I think I have seen
What I wanted to see.
Goodnight! Sleep well

Thomas Decker

29   A baby is a European

A baby is a European,
He does not eat our food:
He drinks from his own water pot.

A baby is a European,
He does not speak our tongue:
He is cross when the mother understands him not.

A baby is a European,
He cares very little for others;
He forces his will upon his parents.

A baby is a European,
He is always very sensitive:
The slightest scratch on his skin results in an ulcer.

Ewe

30   Kidnapped

[*A village is raided, and some children are disobedient . . .*]

Child, stop crying, stop crying	Zemilize
Our mother told us not to make a fire	Zemilize
But we made a fire	Zemilize
Our mother told us not to let smoke escape	Zemilize
But we let smoke escape	Zemilize

36

Our father told us not to sneeze	Zemilize
But we sneezed	Zemilize
Our father told us not to whisper	Zemilize
But we whispered	Zemilize
Our father told us not to leave home	Zemilize
But we left home	Zemilize
Then a thief stole us	Zemilize
As a hawk steals a chicken	Zemilize
The world picked us	Zemilize
As a bird picks maize	Zemilize
Then we were benighted	Zemilize
In broad day-light.	Zemilize

Igbo

31 Medicine man, I plead with you

Medicine man I come to you
Alugbinrin
Full of penitence;
Alugbinrin
That drug that you gave to me
Alugbinrin
You warned me not to taste of it
Alugbinrin
You warned me not to stub my toes
Alugbinrin
Lest I should spill it on the ground.
Alugbinrin
'Twas a root on my path
That made me stumble so
And spill the precious drug;
Alugbinrin
My hand by accident
On the wet ground it fell;
Alugbinrin
And when I licked my fingers
Behold my tummy swelled.
Medicine man, I plead with you,
Save me from my awful plight.
Alugbinrin.

Mabel Segun (translated)

32   The poor man

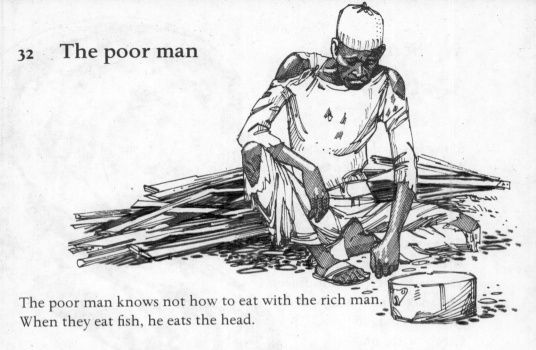

The poor man knows not how to eat with the rich man.
When they eat fish, he eats the head.

Invite a poor man and he rushes in licking his lips and
upsetting the plates.

The poor man has no manners, he comes along with the blood of
lice under his nails.

The face of the poor man is lined from the hunger and thirst
in his belly.

Poverty is no state for any mortal man.
It makes him a beast to be fed on grass.

Poverty is unjust. If it befalls a man, though he is nobly
born, he has no power with God.

Kiswahili

33 Sensemayá

[Song to kill a snake]

Mayombe – bombe – mayombé!
Mayombe – bombe – mayombé!
Mayombe – bombe – mayombé!
The snake has eyes of glass.
The snake appears and it winds around the post.
With eyes of glass around the post,
With her eyes of glass,
The snake creeps without feet.
The snake hides in the grass,
Hides creeping in grass,
Creeps without feet.
Mayombe – bombe – mayombé!
Mayombe – bombe – mayombé!
Mayombe – bombe – mayombé!
Give her the axe and she dies:
Give it her now!
Don't give her the foot, for she bites,
Don't give her the foot, for she runs.

Sensemayá, the snake,
sensemayá.
Sensemayá with the eyes,
sensemayá.
Sensemayá with the tongue,
sensemayá.
Sensemayá with the mouth,
sensemayá.

The dead snake does not eat,
The dead snake does not hiss,
Does not creep,
Does not run,
The dead snake does not drink,
The dead snake does not look;
Does not breathe,
Does not bite.
Mayombe – bombe – mayombé!
Sensemayá, the snake
Mayombe – bombe – mayombé!
Sensemayá does not move,
Mayombe – bombe – mayombé!
Sensemayá the snake.
Mayombe – bombe – mayombé!
Sensemayá is dead.

Nicolás Guillén

41

34 Fading beauty

This flower
dried and crumbled
was once the
darling of the eyes;
That cutlass
worn to the handle
was once a terror
to the trees!
And the rag atop
the dung hill
was once a
party dress.
Now your beauty
bursts in freshness;
Can it bloom
and never fade?

Oluwole Adejare

35   The wise man

The bean of a wise fellow makes cake.
Let me tell you what the world is like:
Two friends living in one room,
One has talent for spending,
One has talent for saving.
The first spends all,
The second saves all,
The unwise one shall perish in the ocean;
The bean of the wise man makes cake.

Twin Seven Seven

36　Shaka Zulu

Shaka was the Great Elephant who stamped his
enemies to dust. He was the Lion of Lions who
gobbled up the sons of Zwide. The Thunder of Zulu
in Heaven sounded throughout the land. He sent
Ntombasi the skull-gatherer to the hyenas. He
smelled out the bloodstench of Nobela the Witch.
He united the warring tribes of Nguniland to build
the greatest empire Africa had ever known.

F. M. Mulikita

37   The Creator

He is patient, he is not angry.
He sits in silence to pass judgement.
He sees you even when he is not looking.
He stays in a far place – but his eyes are on the town.

He stands by his children and lets them succeed.
He causes them to laugh – and they laugh.
Ohoho – the father of laughter.
His eye is full of joy.
He rests in the sky like a swarm of bees.
Obatala – who turns blood into children.

Yoruba

38　A Zulu lyric

[*First speaker*]　　　　　Take off your hat.

[*Second speaker*]　　　　What is your home name?

[*Third speaker*]　　　　Who is your father?

[*First speaker*]　　　　Who is your chief?

[*Second speaker*]　　　　Where do you pay your tax?

[*Third speaker*]　　　　What river do you drink?

[*Fourth and fifth
speakers together*]　　　We mourn for our country.

Zulu

39　The guerillas

[*For the fighting men in Southern Africa*]

There is such a pleasure at last
in handling a cool efficient weapon
most modern, highly automatic
and moving off at the ready –
wishing they could see at home – the friends
and especially the children,
and imagining the deeds of flame and terror
– terror from this weapon, terrible and cold.

Dennis Brutus

40   Freedom

Many days have passed –
They will wake and come again.
We are a master people, a free people.

Pygmy

Teacher's notes

1 Under the mango tree Whenever possible in this anthology, poems should be *sung*. This poem is here for the sole purpose of singing and enjoyment. Many teachers will know the traditional tune that goes with the original English version of this song (*Old Roger is dead . . .*) but any tune chosen by the teacher would do.

2 Fine, big yam Again, to be sung and enjoyed. (The tune of *Three blind mice* can be used to make it a rousing round!) Discuss: Which do you prefer to carry – yams or firewood? Why? Why do farmers feel proud to show people their yams? How do you plant yams? What is your favourite way of cooking and serving yam? (Pupils can write down their answer after discussing it with the teacher.)

3 Lullaby Read this moving little poem aloud with as much expression as possible. Get a good pupil to read it aloud – the whole class can join in on *but you are mine* as a kind of chorus. Discuss: What does the speaker feel about her child? Should children *ever* be taken away from their parents, e.g. to live with their grandparents? (Encourage a good argument on this point.) If the child could answer back, what might his reply be? (Later, if you like, get them to write down their answer, perhaps beginning: *I wouldn't leave you/Even if . . . Even if . . .* etc.)

4 Kikuyu lullaby This was adapted from one in Taban lo Liyong's *Popular Culture of East Africa* (Longman 1972). This well illustrates the problem of translation: it is impossible to translate the original Kikuyu poem literally; moreover, the original version contains various sounds and stylistic devices that English cannot do justice to. The version in this book is an attempt to capture something of the spirit and sound of the original – both are regarded as more important than literal meaning. Both teachers, and pupils may, it is hoped, be encouraged to try similar experiments in adapting poems from their own language. *Irungu* is of course the name of the child. *Urururu* and the *u* sounds are meant to sooth the baby.

   gruel – porridge

5 Song of a motherless child To be read aloud both by teacher and pupils. Discuss any difficult words and: Do you think *my father's wife* is kind to the child? What does the child hope for? Do you feel sorry for the child? Why? What do you feel about the woman? What can we learn from this poem?

Nda – Igbo, like many other African languages, has a sort of "sound-tag" at the end of songs and poems.

Note: This poem, and number **30** in this collection, come from an article "Igbo Traditional Poetry and Family Relationships" by R. Egudu (*African Studies* 32.1 1973).

6 Riddles   To be read aloud and discussed. It may be best to let them find the answers for homework: this may encourage the pupils to use a little English outside the classroom! Answers: 1 A black mamba (Luo). 2 A fish (Fulani). 3 A cooking pot (Kikuyu). 4 A comb (Kiswahili). 5 A fire (Kikuyu). 6 The hump on a cow (Kamba). 7 A maize cob (Ganda). 8 A sailing boat (Kiswahili).

7 The lazy farmer   This poem is based on an incident described in A, Madumere's article "Ibo Village Music" (p. 64 of *African Affairs* 52 1953), quoted in Ruth Finnegan's *Oral Literature in Africa* (Oxford 1970) p. 278. This time there is no attempt to capture the form of the original – but it is hoped that something of the Umuahia *oro* songs is caught. The poem should be read aloud and discussed: Did the wife behave correctly? Do you think the neighbours were right to blame the husband? What can we learn from this story?

8 Pick a bale o' cotton   Originally sung by Negro slave cotton pickers in the USA. Its speed tries to match that of the pickers' hands, as they move among the dry bolls. No one has ever managed to pick a bale of cotton in one day (about 800 kilograms). Perhaps the best workers could "snatch" was 250–290 kilos between sun-up and sundown.

To be read aloud, and enjoyed. This poem gives particularly good rhythm training. The leader – teacher or pupil – can sing the first and third lines; the chorus can join in on the rest. Discuss: Would Ibejimato have been a good cotton picker?

9 Mountain, let me pass   This seems to be an example of a traditional poem being adapted into English. It was written by a twelve-year-old Ghanaian boy, and shows that children are capable of impressive results when they try to write their own poetry. Discuss the picture: Who can see the mountain's face and hands? Let the pupils draw a mountain.

pesewas – small Ghanaian coins.

10 Tortoise seeks wisdom   Here a traditional story is retold in the form of a *ballad*. A ballad is a story retold in verses of four lines each; two or more of the lines may rhyme. Read the poem aloud, and then get the pupils to retell it with their books closed. Then get pupils to read it aloud. One can be the story-teller, one the tortoise, and one the stranger. Discuss: What did Tortoise try to do? Why did he fail to climb the tree? What did the stranger tell him? Why did Tortoise break the gourd? What can we learn from this story?

This is the kind of story that the story-teller in the village might have told. Encourage the pupils to tell similar stories – both in speech and writing. If they write a story get them to illustrate it too, with either pictures or models.

This story could also be acted.

11 Tintingun   Explain to the children that *orogun* is a stick made out of the midrib of the palm branch. It is used for stirring yam flour in boiling water until the yam becomes *amala* (a kind of thick porridge).

Many traditional stories have a *refrain*, or some kind of chorus, or song, in the middle. This is one example; it again shows how a translation involves a degree of adaptation. This refrain makes an enjoyable exercise in reading aloud – with everyone joining in for the chorus *Tintingun*!

12 Crossing a busy street   This poem by a twelve-year-old child may encourage some of your pupils to try their hand at writing, too. Discuss: Why is it hard to cross the road in a town or city? Should cars go fast in built-up areas? What two things should you NEVER do according to this poem? What should you do whenever you cross the road? What is the Highway Code?

13 When it is raining   Again, this little poem will encourage your pupils to write their own pieces. Discuss: What do the children do if they are caught on the road by the rain? How might you make an umbrella if you don't have one?

Encourage the pupils to make up some lines of their own beginning: *When it is raining*. The second line might begin with any of the following: *The sky . . . The temperature . . . The air . . . Everyone . . . The children . . . The farm . . .* etc.

14 When the electric lights are out   Discuss different ways of lighting a house or room at night. Which is the best? the cheapest? the most reliable? What can we learn from this poem?

15 The trouble-lover   To be read loud and enjoyed! The poem can also be acted or mimed. Discuss: What sort of thing does Ojo the Trouble-Lover do? Have any of the pupils met this kind of person? Get them to talk about similar characters or incidents. Why is it wrong to quarrel? What should one try to do instead? What should you do if someone tries to "pick a fight" with you? (Many answers are possible, this question should provoke an interesting discussion.)

Get the pupils to write about and draw some other "village character" e.g. a farmer; a blacksmith; a medicine man; a drummer.

16 Rain music   To be read aloud and enjoyed particularly for its regular rhythm, its rhymes, and its colourful language. Discuss with the class the way the poet sees the world as a drum, and the rain as drumsticks. Who is the drummer? Notice how the rhythm of the poem sounds like a drum. Get some of the pupils to read it aloud while the others beat time with two fingers of one hand in the palm of the other.

17 The flower is broken   Written by a twelve-year-old boy who had previously shown a marked reluctance to write. The poem may mean different things to different people: maybe the changing seasons, or the continuing cycle of life and death; but it looks at the world in a new way, and uses language in a new way. Some pupils may like to write experimental poems of their own – perhaps beginning with the line *The flower is broken/dead/dying*, or with some other equally "strong" opening line the teacher may like to think up. (Other possibilities include *The cow is giving birth, The rain has started, The vultures are circling, The fire is glowing*, etc.)

18 A male lion, I roar   Talk to the class about lions. Explain that this poem was originally written in Kiswahili: the "speaker" is a lion. The poem should be read aloud in a very proud, bold manner; it seems that all the hunters are afraid of the lion, and perhaps are changing their minds about hunting it! Discuss: Has anyone seen a lion, leopard or similar animal? Get them to talk about it. What are lions like? What would you do if you met one? Is this lion in the poem afraid?

ripe – fruit *ripens*; but in this case, *the ripe* are men who are fully mature, or brave. *raw* – lions eat *raw* meat (uncooked). In this case, *the raw* are men who are not prepared, inexperienced, or afraid.

19 You will walk in peace   Discuss the meaning of the word *superstition* with the class. Then read the poem aloud in a menacing tone of voice. Discuss: What four things does the poet warn us against? Do you believe him? Perhaps the pupils can think of other common superstitions, particularly those to do with death or night! Encourage them to talk about these, and discuss how far these beliefs may be justified.

embalmed – preserved

Perhaps some of the pupils would like to try writing a poem about local beliefs or superstitions – perhaps using this framework: *Never . . . For if you do, . . .*

20 The hairy toe   Pupils find this poem both terrifying and enormous fun at the same time. It should be read aloud in as dramatic a manner as possible. Later, the pupils will also greatly enjoy reading it in a similar manner – and there will be hot competition as to who should read the Voice! Again, this poem could be mimed or acted: if desired, the woman could have a husband she could talk to, to discuss her "find" in the fields. Discuss: Do you think the woman behaved wisely, or foolishly? What do you think happened at the end? Do you think this is a true story? Activity: Draw the monster. Write a similar "horror" poem.

21 The snake-man and the girl   This story occurs in various forms all over Africa. It is ideal for acting purposes.

The *cave* could simply be a table or desk. Suitors could enter and leave stage left. After the marriage-dance, the family could leave, or better still, crouch down and look the other way as the girl and her husband go to the cave. They would then be ready to hear the bad news from the friendly bird.

This play might actually be acted to junior classes. Alternatively, perhaps the pupils could make up or improvise a performance of another traditional story.

22 Mocking song   This song comes from the Sudan, but this type of song can be found in many parts of Africa. Note that the first verse can be read by one group, the second by another. They can all read the last line!

glutton – person with an enormous appetite for food.

This poem can, if desired, lead to a discussion of the pupils' ideal marriage partner – the qualities they would like to find in him or her.

23 The lazy man   Discuss: What does the lazy man say when the cock crows? Does he get up immediately? What does he do? What happens while he is still half-asleep? How does he get his food? Why will his breastbone stick out if there is no sacrifice? What is the poem's attitude to the lazy man? What can we learn from this poem? Perhaps some of the pupils might like to make up a similar mocking song about *The greedy man, The mean man, The dishonest trader*, or some other character!

24 My lively young man   Read the poem aloud – the whole class can join in line 3 of each verse. Discuss: What words does the writer use to describe the young man? (List them on the board, and discuss their meaning.) What did he do wrong? What happened to him in the end? What lesson can we learn?

25 Hausa song (from *Black Orpheus* 19)   Discuss: Do you think that the girl really wanted to escape? Give reasons for your answer! How do (a) boys and (b) girls, feel about marriage? Do they look forward to it, or postpone it for as long as possible. Give reasons for your answer! When is the best time in one's life to get married? In what ways should one be prepared before marriage?

26 Song by a woman giving birth   This poem is more suitable for girls. Discuss: What does the singer mean by *In my net I have caught a little bird*? What does she mean by *My heart is caught in the net*? It may be a good way to start a discussion on motherhood with them.

27 Praise of a child   Discuss: What does the poet think of children? What is the meaning of the two lines beginning *The buttocks . . .*? (We love and care for our children regardless of their faults.) *One must not rejoice too soon . . .* Why? What does this mean? Activity: Add a few more lines to the poem on the same subject. Write a similar praise poem called: *Praise of a mother/father*.

28 Sleep well   "Krio is an English-based *Lingua franca* used throughout Sierra Leone as an inter-tribal language of trade and social communication." (Eldred Jones). It is the mother tongue of many in that country. It has also borrowed many words from Yoruba and other African languages. Here is the original version of this charming poem:

Slip gud o, bebi-gial!   A wan foh si da tin   So! set you yai nau noh.
opjin yai lilibit   we kin de shain insai   a tink se a dohn si
en luk mi wan minit   insai yu fain-fain yai wetin a wan foh si
bifo yu slip.   enkoht mi at.   Gudnait! Slip gud!

If you have girls in the class, get one girl to sit in front of the class rocking a "baby" (e.g. a doll) to sleep, while another girl reads the poem aloud.

29 A baby is a European   This clever little poem manages to be on two different subjects at the same time! It is worth discussing how far the pupils agree with it. Discuss: In what ways does the poem say that babies and Europeans are similar? Does the poem list any *good* things about babies? Obtain a list of good things about babies from the class, and write them on the board, e.g. they are beautiful, we love them etc.

Activity: Let the pupils write a poem about babies, beginning e.g. *A baby is a gift from God* . . . etc. If they like, they may try to translate a similar poem from their mother tongue.

30 Kidnapped   This poem shows the results of disobedience during a raid on a village. Perhaps the story could be made the basis for a short mime or play; or artwork.

benighted – overtaken by night, i.e. disaster. What is the moral of this poem?

31 Medicine man, I plead with you   Before treating this poem, tell the class the story of Tortoise who went to see a medicine man because his wife, Yanrinbo, was barren. Tortoise was given a pot of medicine, but was warned not to taste it. The medicine was mixed with some food, and on the way home he felt hungry, so he tasted a little. It was delicious. So he went a bit further, then stopped and tasted some more – and so on, until all the food was eaten. Then his belly began to swell like that of a pregnant woman. Tortoise was very frightened, and he went back to the medicine man; but instead of telling the truth, he tried to make excuses! Discuss: What can we learn from this poem? Talk about medicine men.

32 The poor man   This poem is very effective, and rather moving, when read aloud well. Discuss: In some tribes, the head of a fish is considered a delicacy. In this case, it is clear that the poor man only gets the left-overs! Why does he rush in *licking his lips and upsetting the plates*? (Because he is so hungry.) He is afflicted by lice because he has no proper place to wash. The message of the poem is that poverty is degrading – it makes a person look and behave like *a beast*. What advice can we give to a poor man? Activity: Look at the verse beginning *The face* . . . Can they think of similar lines one could write about (1) *The hands of a poor man* . . . (2) *The feet* . . . (3) *The clothes* . . .

54

33 Sensemayá [*Song to kill a snake*]   This is a very good rhythm poem. The words in italics may be read by the whole class, or a group. The poem could also be danced, sung and acted.

34 Fading beauty   From *Sokoti*, magazine of the University of Ife writers' workshop. To be read aloud. The four groups of lines in the poem may be read by four different people. What can we learn from this poem? If possible bring into class a crumbled flower, an old cutlass (or machete), and a piece of rag.

35 The wise man   (From *Black Orpheus* 22.) Discuss: In what way are the two friends different? The first and last lines are an African proverb. What does it mean? (Be thrifty: "Take care of the pennies, and the pounds will take care of themselves." – This old English proverb can be translated into local currency!) This may lead to a discussion on how and why we should save money. (Savings accounts of various kinds.)

36 Shaka Zulu   Good practice for declamatory reading aloud. This extract is taken from the play *Shaka Zulu* by F. M. Mulikita (Longman). Shaka was of course the great Zulu warrior king. Read the play if you want to know more about him! (It could also be acted.)

Zwide – a great but treacherous Nguni chief whose sons were defeated in battle by Shaka's armies.

Ntombasi – Zwide's witch-like mother; in her hut she kept the heads of thirty chiefs killed by her son. She claimed to have magic powers even over animals; Shaka killed her by locking her inside a hut with a hyena.

Nobela – A witch employed by Shaka to "smell out" traitors, he proved her "magic" powers were false. She took poison to escape his punishment.

Shaka, King of the Zulu by R. Woolley (Longman Makers of African History) is also a very readable account of his life. (It could be read to the class a chapter at a time.)

37 The Creator   According to the traditional religion of the Yoruba people, Obatala was the God of Creation. Again, this poem gives good practice in reading aloud. Discuss: Do you know any stories about Obatala? How do worshippers of Obatala dress? (In white cloth.) Find out more about the legend of how Obatala created men. (See *Tales of Yoruba Gods and Heroes*, Courlander Crown Publishing Inc. N.Y. 1973.) Alternatively, discuss other "creation myths" that the children know: this could be the basis for a class project – either a play, or a wall frieze.

38 A Zulu lyric   This little poem tells us in the simplest possible way, that of a short conversation, about the situation in South Africa, where black people are oppressed by a white minority government. The first six lines represent the kinds of thing that are said by the bureaucrats of an oppressive government machine – rude, bossy, interfering, unnecessary – and should be fired peremptorily at the 4th and 5th speakers, who should stand looking dejected. As it stands, the last line is an understatement of the despair that many blacks in South Africa feel, and should be delivered as eloquently as possible.

39 The guerillas   by Dennis Brutus, who was born in Salisbury, Zimbabwe. In South Africa he fought against the government's policy of *apartheid* (or separate development), and was imprisoned with hard labour for his efforts. He is now in exile in the USA; but continues his fight against South Africa's racial policies.

   This poem, an extract from a longer one, gives a good idea of what it is like to be a freedom-fighter (or *guerilla*). Talk to the class about S. Africa, and the freedom-fighters (see the picture). Then read the poem aloud. Treat any difficult words:
handling – holding, or carrying.
cool – metal feels cool.
weapon – gun, in this case.
automatic – i.e. if you press the trigger, it fires many bullets, not just one.
at the ready – the man is holding his gun *at the ready* – in case of attack!
imaging – imagining, or thinking about.
   Read the poem again, and discuss: What are the feelings of the freedom-fighter in this poem? (Pleasure in being able to fight back; wishing he could see home; imagining the deeds to come; a business-like attitude; hatred; the longing for home of an exile.)

40 Freedom   Often the simplest, shortest statement is the best. This little song comes from the pygmies of Cameroon and Gabon.

Acknowledgements

We are grateful to the following for permission to reproduce copyright material:

The author, Samuel Adatsi (aged 12 years) for "Mountain let me pass"; Allen and Unwin Ltd., for an extract from "The guerillas" by Dennis Brutus from *Poets to the People* by Barry Feisberg; Cambridge University Press for an extract from "Invocation of the Creator" a traditional poem translated by Ulli Beier and "The lazy man" from *African Poetry* p. 57 by Ulli Beier; Mrs Yomi Decker for the original Krio version of "Slip gud" by the late Thomas Decker; Drum Publications Ltd., for "A Zulu lyric" translated by Hugh Tracey from *Darkness and Light*; Éditions Seghers for "Tu marcheras en paix" by Martial Sinda from *A Book of African Verse* edited by Reed and Wake; The Essex Music Group for "Pick a bale o' cotton" words and music by Huddie Ledbetter; Collected and adapted by John A. Lomax and Alan Lomax © 1936 and renewed 1964 Folkways Music Publishers Inc., by permission of Kensington Music Ltd.; the author, Neville Grant for "Fine, big yam", "The lazy farmer" (based on an *oro* song) and "The snake-man and the girl"; Ibadan University Press for an adapted version of "The trouble-lover" by Adeboye Babalola in *The Anthology of West African Verse* edited by Olumbe Bassir; Longman Group Ltd., for an extract inspired by "Riddles" in *The Popular Culture of East Africa* by Taban Lo Liyong, and "Kikuyu lullaby" adapted from a translation of a traditional Kikuyu song appears in *Popular Culture of East Africa* by Taban Lo Liyong; and an extract translated by Eldred Jones from *The English Language in West Africa*; Mbari Club for "Lullaby" translated by Rwabena Nketia and "Sensemayá" by Nicolás Guillén translated by S. Akaifi appears in *Black Orpheus No 3*; "Hausa song" translated by S. Rabeh appears in *Black Orpheus No 19*, "The wise man" by Twin Seven Seven translated by Ulli Beier in *Black Orpheus No 22*, "Praise of a Child" translated by Bakare Gbadamosi and Ulli Beier from *The Moon Cannot Fight*; the author, Joel Mensah (aged 12 years) for "The flower is broken"; The Ministry of Information Ghana for "A baby is a European" a traditional Ewe poem translated by Kafu Hoh appears in *Voices of Ghana*; Oxford University Press for an extract from *Swahili Poetry* by Lyndon Harries © Oxford University Press 1962. Reprinted by permission of Oxford University Press; the author, Modupe Oyedele for an adapted version of "My lively young man"; Peter Pauper Press Inc., for an extract from a traditional Sudanese poem p. 10 from *African Poems and Love Songs* by Charlotte and Wolf Leslau; the author, Femi Segun (aged 8 years) for "When it is raining"; the author, Mabel Segun for "Tortoise seeks wisdom", "Tintingun" translated by Mabel Segun from a Yoruba poem, and "Medicine man, I plead with you" translated by Mabel Segun from a traditional Yoruba poem; the author, Omowunmi Segun (aged 12 years) for "Crossing a busy street"; Sokoti Magazine for an adapted version of "Let us in darkness dwell" and an adapted version of "Crumbling flower" by Oluwole Adejare from *Sokoti Magazine*; Mr Willard Trask and Macmillan Publishing Co. Inc., for an extract from "Song sung by a woman while giving birth" and "Many days have passed" from *The Unwritten Song* Vol I edited and with translations by Willard R. Trask © 1966 by Willard Trask; The University of Wisconsin Press for "A male lion, I roar" translated and edited by Lyndon Harries, *Poems from Kenya: Gnomic Verses in Swahili* by Ahmad Nassir bin Juma Bhalo (Madison: University of Wisconsin Press © 1966 by the Regents of the University of Wisconsin) p. 41; Witwatersrand University Press and Professor R. N. Egudu for an extract from "Song of a motherless child" and "Igbo Traditional Poetry and Family Relationships" by R. N. Egudu, *African Studies* 32 1973 pp. 15–24 with the permission of the Witwatersrand University Press, Johannesburg.

Sources

1 "Under the mango tree" adapted from a traditional English poem 2 "Fine, big yam" by Neville Grant
3 "Lullaby" translated by Rwabena Nketia, appears in *Black Orpheus No 3*, published by Longman Group Ltd.
4 "Kikuyu lullaby" adapted from a translation of a traditional Kikuyu song, appears in *Popular Culture of East Africa*
by Taban lo Liyong, published by Longman Group Ltd. 5 "Song of a motherless child" translated from a
traditional Igbo poem, appears in "Igbo Traditional Poetry and Family Relationships" by Romanus Egudu *African
Studies Journal* Vol 32 No 1 1973 6 "Riddles" adapted from translated riddles that appear in *Popular Culture of East Africa*
by Taban lo Liyong, published by Longman Group Ltd. 7 "The lazy farmer" by Neville Grant, based on an *oro song*
8 "Pick a bale o' cotton" words and music by Huddie Ledbetter; Collected and adapted by John A. Lomax and Alan
Lomax. Tro (the Essex Music Group) © 1936 and renewed 1964 Folkways Music Publishers Inc., by permission of
Kensington Music Ltd. 9 "Mountain let me pass" by Samuel Adatsi (aged 12 years) 10 "Tortoise seeks wisdom" by
Mabel Segun 11 "Tintingun" translated by Mabel Segun from a Yoruba poem 12 "Crossing a busy street" by
Omowunmi Segun (aged 12 years) 13 "When it is raining" by Femi Segun (aged 8 years) 14 "When the electric
lights are out" adapted from "Let us in darkness dwell" by Oluwole Adejare, published by *Sokoti Magazine* 15 "The
trouble-lover" (adapted) by Adeboye Babalola from *The Anthology of West African Verse* edited by Olumbe Bassir,
published by Ibadan University Press 16 "Rain music" by Joseph S. Cotter Jnr. 17 "The flower is broken" by Joel
Mensah (aged 12 years) 18 "A male lion, I roar" by Ahmed Nassir Bin Juma Bhalo, translated by Lyndon Harries,
appears in *Poems of Kenya* Gnomic Verses in Swahili by Ahmad Nassir Bin Juma Bhalo, translated by Lyndon Harries,
published by University of Wisconsin Press © 1966 by the Regents of the University of Wisconsin p. 41 19 "You will
walk in peace" from "Tu marcheras en paix" by Martial Sinda, in *A Book of African Verse* edited by Reed and Wake,
published by Éditions Seghers 20 "The hairy toe" – Traditional American 21 "The snake-man and the girl" by
Neville Grant 22 "Mocking song" – Traditional Sudan poem appears in *African Poems and Love Songs* by Charlotte and
Wolf Leslau, published by Peter Pauper Press 23 "The lazy man" – Traditional Yoruba poem appears in *African
Poetry* by Ulli Beier, published by Cambridge University Press 24 "My lively young man" by Modupe Oyedele
(adapted) 25 "Hausa song" – Traditional Hausa song translated by S. Rabeh, appears in *Black Orpheus No 19*,
published by Longman Group Ltd. 26 "Song by a woman giving birth" – Traditional Pygmy song translated by
Willard Trask, from *The Unwritten Song* edited by Willard Trask, published by Macmillan Publishing Co. Inc.
27 "Praise of a child" – Traditional Yoruba poem translated by Ulli Beier and Bakare Gbadamosi 28 "Sleep well" by
Thomas Decker translated by Eldred Jones 29 "A baby is a European" – Traditional Ewe poem translated by Kafu
Hoh, appears in *Voices of Ghana* 30 "Kidnapped" – Traditional Igbo poem translated by Romanus Egudu in "Igbo
Traditional Poetry and Family Relationships" *African Studies* Vol 32 No 1 1973 31 "Medicine man, I plead with you" –
Traditional Yoruba poem translated by Mabel Segun 32 "The poor man" – Traditional Swahili poem translated
by Lyndon Harries, appears in *Swahili Poetry*, published by Oxford University Press 33 "Sensemayá" by Nicolás
Guillén translated by S. Akaifi appears in *Black Orpheus No 3* published by Longman Group Ltd. 34 "Fading beauty"
from "Crumbling flower" by Oluwole Adejare appears in *Sokoti Magazine* 35 "The wise man" by Twin Seven Seven
translated by Ulli Beier in *Black Orpheus No 22* published by Longman Group Ltd. 36 "Shaka Zulu" by F. M. Mulikita,
published by Longman Group Ltd. 37 "The Creator" from "Invocation of the Creator" translated from Yoruba
by Ulli Beier, from *African Poetry*, published by Cambridge University Press 38 "A Zulu lyric" – Traditional Zulu
poem translated by Hugh Tracey, appears in *Darkness and Light*, published by Drum Publications 39 "The guerillas"
by Dennis Brutus from *Poets to the People* edited by Barry Feisberg, published by George Allen and Unwin
40 "Freedom" translated by Willard Trask from a traditional Pygmy poem appears in *The Unwritten Song* Vol 1
published by Macmillan Publishing Co. Inc.